The 1980s

CW00801889

Exclusive Distributors:
Music Sales Limited
8/9 Frith Street, London W1D 3JB, UK.

Order No. HLE90002759
ISBN 1-84609-361-9
This book © Copyright 2006 by Hal Leonard Europe

Printed in the USA

Your Guarantee of Quality
As publishers, we strive to produce every book to the highest commercial standards.
The book has been carefully designed to minimise awkward page turns and to make playing from it a real pleasure.
Throughout, the printing and binding have been planned to ensure a sturdy, attractive publication which should give years of enjoyment.
If your copy fails to meet our high standards, please inform us and we will gladly replace it.

www.musicsales.com

This publication is not authorised for sale in the United States of America and/or Canada

CONTENTS

ABRACADABRA

Words and Music by
STEVE MILLER

I heat up, ___ I can't cool down. You've got me spin-nin' a-round and 'round. ___

Kiss me, ba - by, let the fire get high - er, _____ yeah, __

_____ yeah, yeah. ___

Guitar solo ad lib.

Play 3 times

AGAINST ALL ODDS
(Take A Look At Me Now)

Words and Music by
PHIL COLLINS

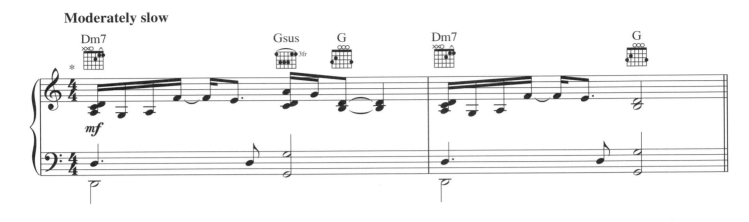

How can I just let you walk a-way, just let you leave with-out __ a trace, when I

stand here tak-ing ev-'ry breath __ with you? ____ Ooh. ____ You're the

* Recorded a half step lower.

'cause I'll ___ still be stand-ing here, ___ and you com-ing back ___

to me ___ is a-gainst ___ all odds, ___ it's the chance I've got - ta take. ___

Take a look at me now. ___

AGAINST THE WIND

Words and Music by
BOB SEGER

noth - in' left _____ to burn _____ and noth - in' left to prove. ___
wor - ried a - bout pay - in', or e - ven how much I owed. ___

End instrumental

And I re - mem - ber what she _____ said to
Mov - in' eight miles a min - ute for months at a
Well, those drift - er's days are _____ past me

me, _____ how she swore _____ that it nev - er would end. ___
time, _____ break - in' all _____ of the rules _____ that would bend, _
now. _____ I've got so _____ much more to _____ think a - bout: _

I re-mem-ber how she held __ me oh so tight, ____
I be-gan to find __ my-self search - in',
dead - lines __ and com - mit - ments,

Wish I did - n't know now what I did-n't know then.
search-in' for shel - ter a - gain and a - gain.
what to leave in, what to leave out.

A - gainst the wind, __
A - gainst the wind, __
A - gainst the wind, __

we were run - nin' a - gainst __ the wind. __
lit - tle some-thin' a - gainst __ the wind. __
I'm still run - nin' a - gainst __ the wind. __

We were
I
I'm

ALL NIGHT LONG
(All Night)

Words and Music by
LIONEL RICHIE

long, _____ Oh. _____ long. _____

Yeah! Once you _ get start - ed _ you can't sit _ down. _

Come join _ the fun, it's _ a mer - ry - go -

round.

Ev - 'ry - one's danc - ing _ their trou - bles _ a -

CALL ME

from the Paramount Motion Picture AMERICAN GIGOLO

Words by DEBORAH HARRY
Music by GIORGIO MORODER

ALMOST PARADISE

Love Theme from the Paramount Motion Picture FOOTLOOSE

Words by DEAN PITCHFORD
Music by ERIC CARMEN

AMANDA

Words and Music by
TOM SCHOLZ

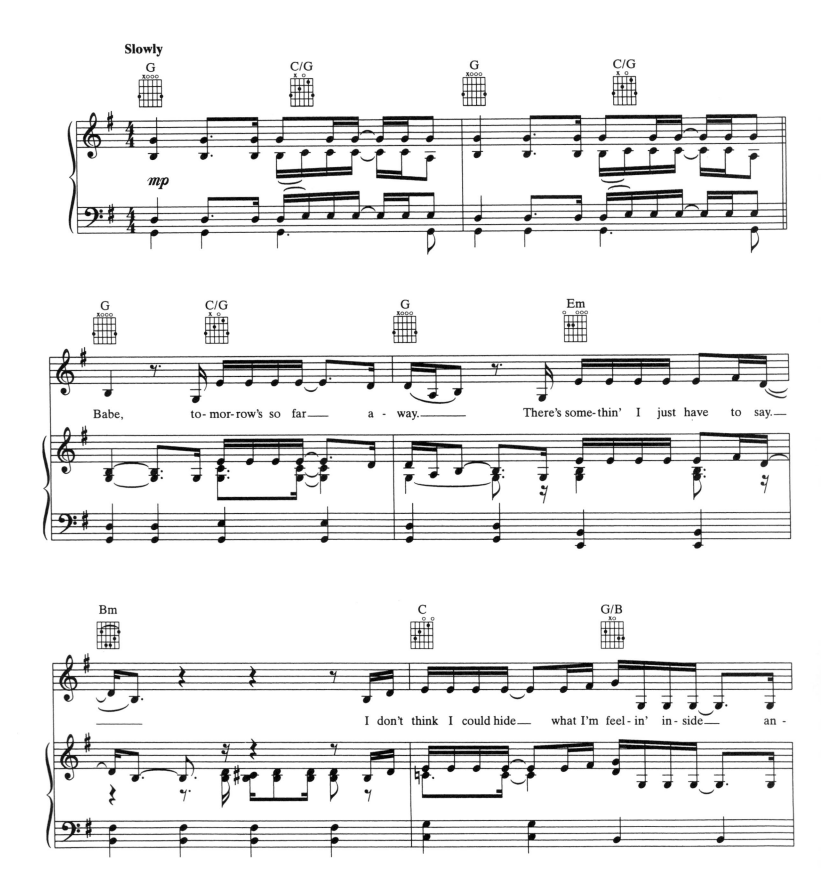

44

You and I,—— I know that we—— can't wait.—— And I swear,—

—— I swear it's not a lie,—— girl. To-mor-row may be too late.——

AXEL F
Theme from the Paramount Motion Picture BEVERLY HILLS COP

By HAROLD FALTERMEYER

Moderately fast, with a strong beat

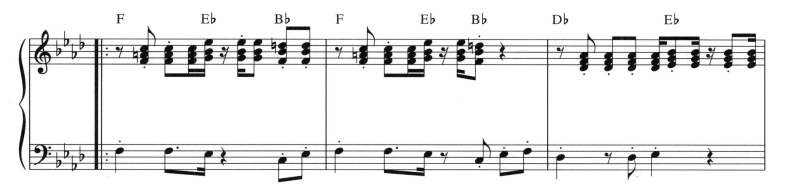

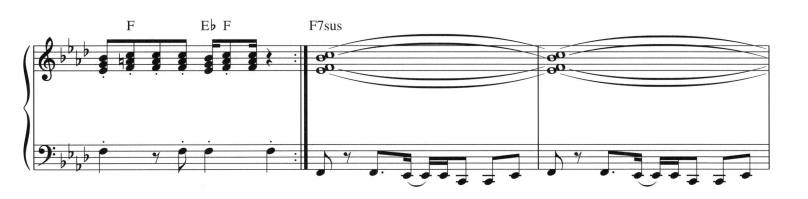

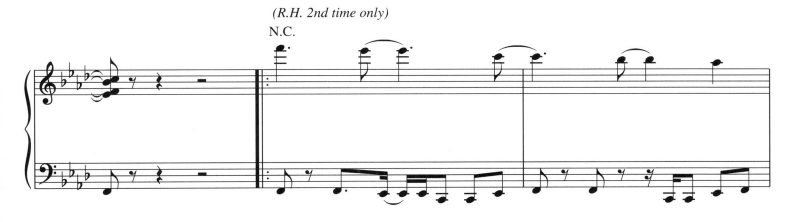

51

BABY, COME TO ME

Words and Music by
ROD TEMPERTON

Think-in' back in time,__ when love was on-ly in the mind,__ I re-al-ize

Spend-in' ev-'ry dime__ to keep you talk-in' on the line,__ that's how it was,

ain't no sec-ond chance;__ you've got to hold on to ro-mance.__ Don't

and all those walks to-geth — er out in an-y kind of weath-er,__ just be-

CENTERFOLD

Written by SETH JUSTMAN

Bright Rock

Lyrics:

Does she walk?_ Does she talk?_ Does she come com-plete?_ My

It's o-kay,_ I un-der-stand,_ this ain't no nev-er-nev-er land. I

home-room, home-room an-gel al-ways pulled me from my seat.

hope that when this is-sue's gone, I'll see you when your clothes are on.

DANGER ZONE
from the Motion Picture TOP GUN

Words and Music by GIORGIO MORODER
and TOM WHITLOCK

Rev - vin' up your en - gine; lis - ten to her howl - in' roar. _____
Head - in' in the twi - light spread - in' out her wings to - night. _____
Out a - long the edge is al - ways where I burn to be. _____

High - way to the dan - ger zone; _____

right in - to the dan - ger zone. _____

Repeat and Fade

DIDN'T WE ALMOST HAVE IT ALL

Words and Music by WILL JENNINGS
and MICHAEL MASSER

Lyrics:

Re-mem-ber when we held on in the rain, the nights we al-most
lost it; once a-gain we can take the night in-to to-

The way you used to touch me felt so fine; we kept our hearts to-
geth-er; down the line, a mo-ment in the soul can last for-

69

DON'T DO ME LIKE THAT

Words and Music by
TOM PETTY

Moderately

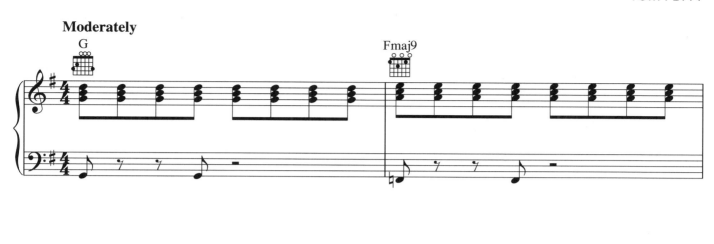

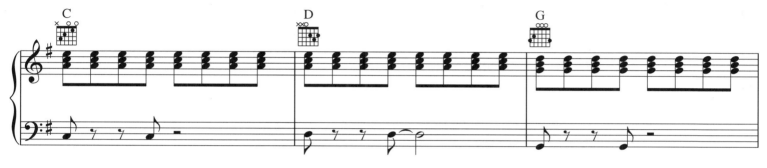

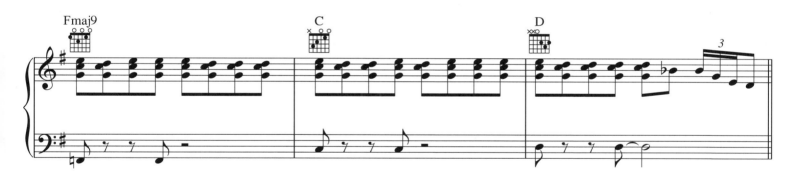

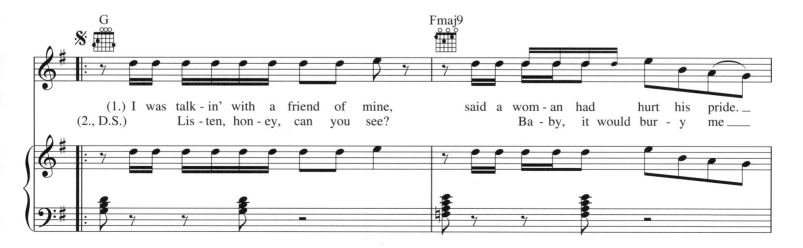

(1.) I was talk-in' with a friend of mine, said a wom-an had hurt his pride. __
(2., D.S.) Lis-ten, hon-ey, can you see? Ba-by, it would bur-y me __

DON'T YOU
(Forget About Me)
from the Universal Picture THE BREAKFAST CLUB

Words and Music by KEITH FORSEY
and STEVE SCHIFF

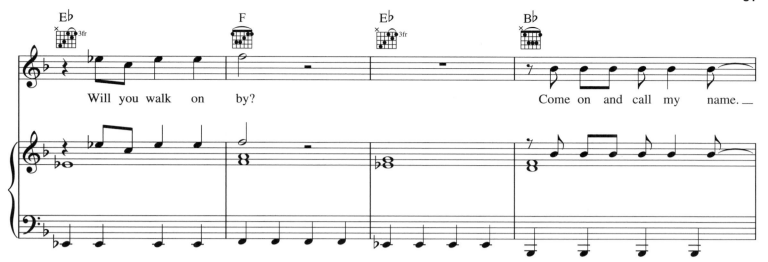

Will you walk on by?   Come on and call my name.____

____   Will you call my name?   I say ooh

la,   la, la, la,_____   la, la, la, la,_____   la, la, la,   la, la,   la, la, la,   la.

DREAMER

Words and Music by RICK DAVIES
and ROGER HODGSON

83

you can do some - thing.) If I could do an - y - thing... _ (But can you do some - thing

Bb/C

out _ of this world?) _

C

Gm7/C

Take a dream on a Sun - day.

cresc. little by little

92

Can you put your hands in your head, oh no! Oh

no!

Fade out

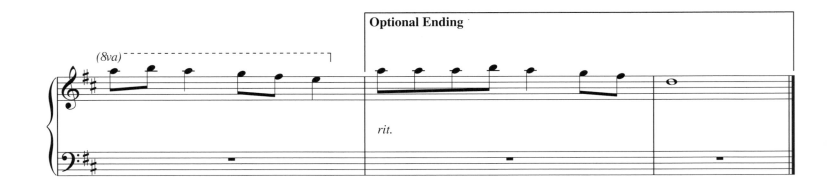

Optional Ending

rit.

EBONY AND IVORY

Words and Music by
PAUL McCARTNEY

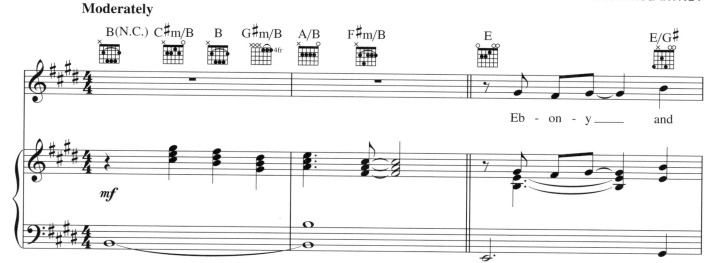

Eb-on-y ___ and

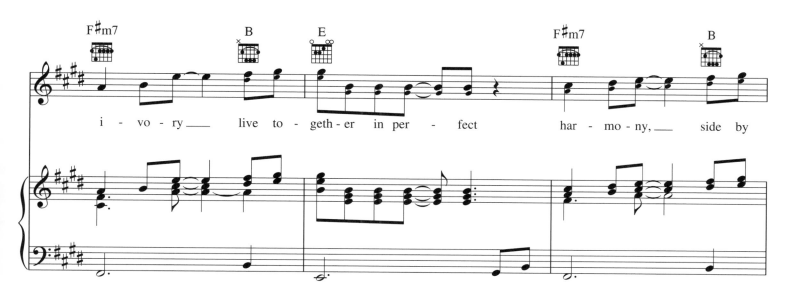

i - vo - ry ___ live to-geth-er in per - fect har-mo-ny, ___ side by

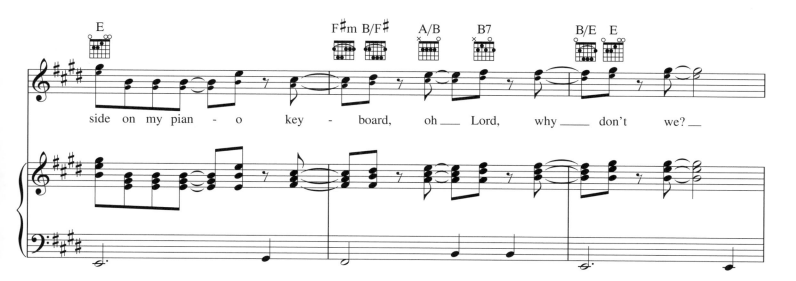

side on my pian - o key - board, oh ___ Lord, why ___ don't we? ___

i - vo - ry ___ live to - geth - er in per - fect har - mo - ny, ___ side by

side on my pian - o key - board, oh ___ Lord, why ___ don't we? ___

To Coda ⊕

Double tempo

Eb - on - y, ___

EVERY BREATH YOU TAKE

Music and Lyrics by
STING

long for your _ em-brace. I keep cry - ing, ba - by, ba - by, please _

FOREVER YOUNG

Words and Music by ROD STEWART, JIM CREGAN,
KEVIN SAVIGAR and BOB DYLAN

round you when you're far ___ from home. ___   And may you

grow ___ to be   proud, ___   dig - ni - fied ___ and   true. ___
for - tune   be   with you, may your   guid - ing   light ___ be   strong, ___
fi - n'lly   fly a - way,   I'll be   hop - ing that I   served ___ you   well. ___

And do un - to oth - ers as
build a stair - way to heav - en with a
For all the wis - dom of a life - time,

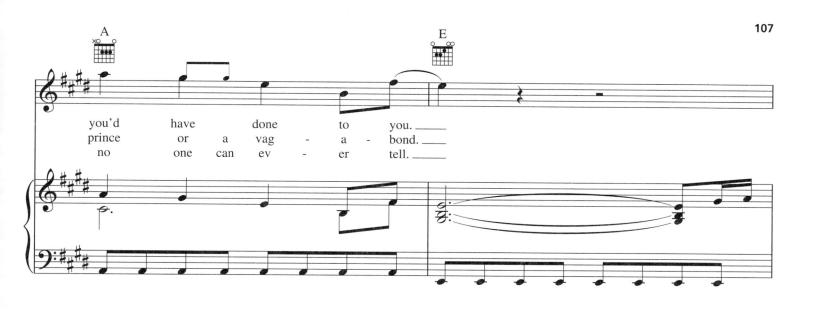

you'd have done to you. _____
prince or a vag - a - bond. _____
no one can ev - er tell. _____

Be cou - ra - geous and _____ be brave. _____
And may you nev - er love _____ in vain. _____
But what - ev - er road _____ you choose, _____

_____ And in my heart you'll al - ways stay _____
_____ And in my heart you will _____ re - main _____
_____ I'm right be - hind you win _____ or lose, _____

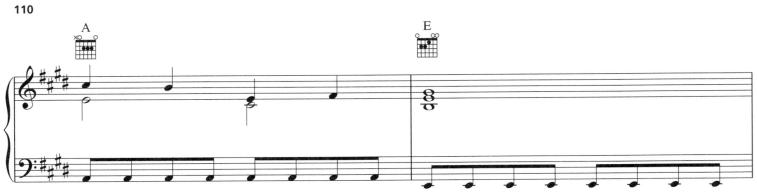

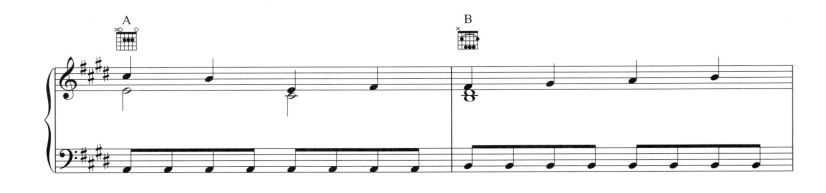

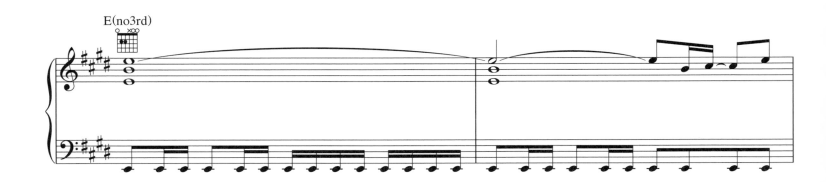

GIVE ME THE NIGHT

Words and Music by
ROD TEMPERTON

Verse 2. You need the evenin' action, a place to dine.
A glass of wine, a little late romance.
It's a chain reaction.
We'll see the people of the world comin' out to dance.
'Cause there's. . . Chorus

Verse 3. (Instrumental)
'Cause there's. . . Chorus

Verse 4. And if we stay together,
We'll feel the rhythm of evening takin' us up high.
Never mind the weather.
We'll be dancin' in the street until the morning light.
'Cause there's. . . Chorus

HARD HABIT TO BREAK

Words and Music by STEPHEN KIPNER
and JOHN LEWIS PARKER

I guess I thought you'd be ____ here for - ev - er;
found some - one else; you had ____ ev - 'ry rea - son.

an - oth - er il - lu - sion I chose to cre - ate. ____ You
You know I can't blame you for run - nin' to him. ____ Two

HARD TO SAY I'M SORRY

Words and Music by PETER CETERA
and DAVID FOSTER

123

HEARTBREAKER

Words and Music by CLIFF WADE
and GEOFF GILL

Your love ___ is like a tid - al wave ___
Your love ___ has set my soul on fire, ___

spin - nin' o - ver my head, ___
burn - in' out ___ of con - trol. ___

drown - in' me ___ in your prom -
You taught ___ me the ways ___

You're the right___ kind of sin-

-ner to re-lease___ my in - ner fan - ta - sy, ___

THE HEAT IS ON

from the Paramount Motion Picture BEVERLY HILLS COP

Words by KEITH FORSEY
Music by HAROLD FALTERMEYER

The heat is on, __ on __ the street. __ The heat is

on. The heat is on.

F7

The heat is... on!

Vocal 1st time only

N.C.

C7

1 - 3

HERE I GO AGAIN

Words and Music by BERNIE MARSDEN
and DAVID COVERDALE

143

HEAVEN

Words and Music by BRYAN ADAMS
and JIM VALLANCE

HIGHER LOVE

Words and Music by WILL JENNINGS
and STEVE WINWOOD

151

152

156

woah. ___ Bring me a high - er ___ love,

bring me a high - er ___ love. ___

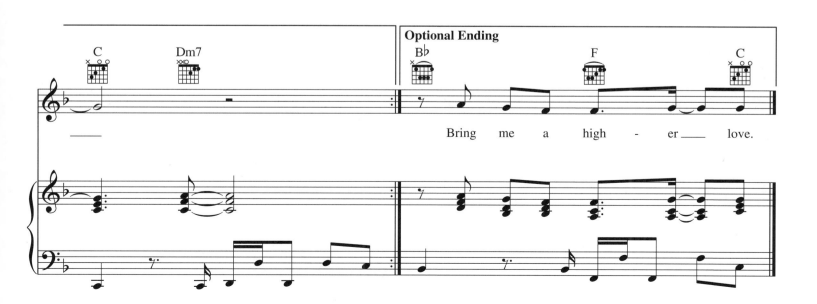

Optional Ending

___ Bring me a high - er ___ love.

HOLD ME NOW

from THE WEDDING SINGER

Words and Music by TOM BAILEY,
ALANNAH CURRIE and JOE LEEWAY

161

HOLD ON LOOSELY

Words and Music by DON BARNES,
JEFF CARLISI and JAMES MICHAEL PETERIK

HOT HOT HOT

Words and Music by
ALPHONSUS CASSELL

Moderate Latin Dance

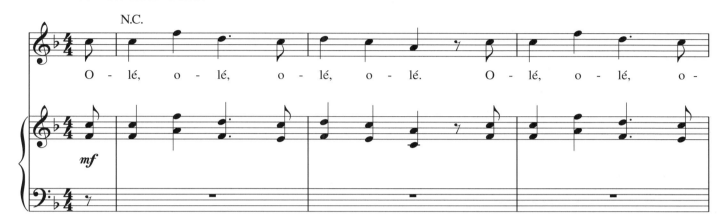

O - lé, o - lé, o - lé, o - lé. O - lé, o - lé, o -

lé, o - lé.

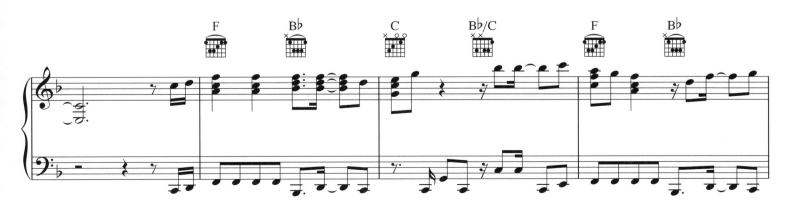

168

HURTS SO GOOD

Words and Music by JOHN MELLENCAMP
and GEORGE GREEN

174

I GUESS THAT'S WHY THEY CALL IT THE BLUES

Words and Music by ELTON JOHN,
BERNIE TAUPIN and DAVEY JOHNSTONE

Moderately slow; with a beat

Don't wish it a-way, don't look at it like it's for -
Just stare in-to space; pic-ture my face in your
Instrumental solo

ev - er.   Be - tween you ___ and
hands. ___   Live for ___ each

I LOVE A RAINY NIGHT

Words and Music by EDDIE RABBITT,
EVEN STEVENS and DAVID MALLOY

181

Show - ers wash __ all my cares a - way, __ I wake up __ to a

sun - ny day, __ 'cause I love __ the rain - y night. It's

I'LL BE THERE FOR YOU

Words and Music by JON BON JOVI
and RICHIE SAMBORA

IF YOU LOVE SOMEBODY
SET THEM FREE

Music and Lyrics by
STING

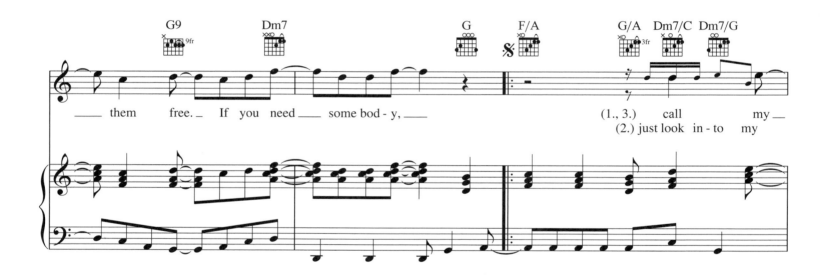

KOKOMO
from the Motion Picture COCKTAIL

Words and Music by MIKE LOVE, TERRY MELCHER,
JOHN PHILLIPS and SCOTT McKENZIE

Moderately bright

A - ru - ba, Ja - mai - ca, oo ___ I wan - na take ya. Ber -

mu - da, Ba - ha - ma, come ___ on, pret - ty ma - ma. Key Lar - go, Mon - te - go, ba -

- by, why don't we go, Ja - mai - ca. Off the Flor - i - da Keys ___
We'll put out to sea ___

Ev - 'ry - bod - y knows _ a lit - tle place like Ko - ko - mo. __

IT'S MY LIFE

Words and Music by MARK DAVID HOLLIS
and TIM FRIESE-GREENE

Moderately fast

It's fun-ny how I ___ find my-self ___ in love ___

___ with you. ___

If I ___ could buy ___ my ___ rea-son-ing,

* *Recorded a half step lower.*

JESSIE'S GIRL

Words and Music by
RICK SPRINGFIELD

KISS ON MY LIST

Words and Music by JANNA ALLEN
and DARYL HALL

220

LADY

Words and Music by
NICHOLAS CALDWELL

You say you love me, la - dy. _____ Girl, I hope you do.

*Recorded a half-step higher.

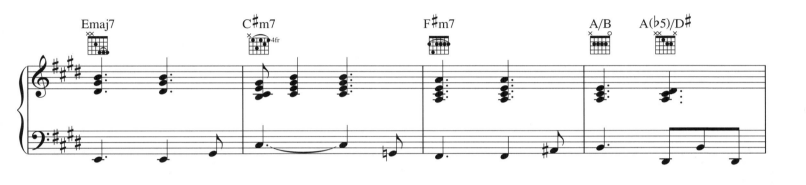

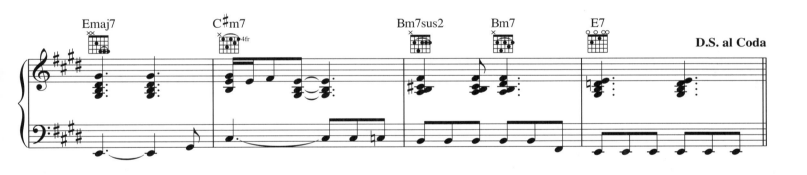

D.S. al Coda

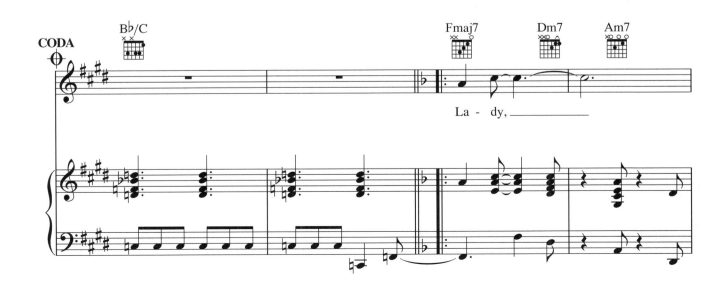

La - dy,

MISSING YOU

Words and Music by JOHN WAITE,
CHARLES SANFORD and MARK LEONARD

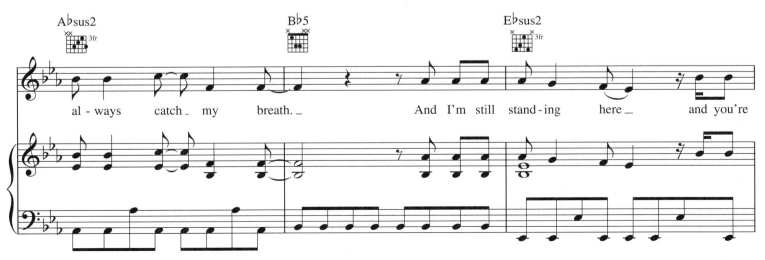

LADY IN RED

Words and Music by
CHRIS DE BURGH

LEGS

Words and Music by BILLY F GIBBONS,
DUSTY HILL and FRANK BEARD

Moderate Rock

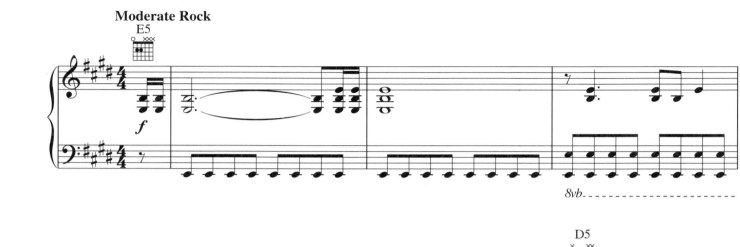

She got ___
She got ___

MAN IN THE MIRROR

Words and Music by GLEN BALLARD
and SIEDAH GARRETT

254

been an - y clear - er. If you wan - na make the world a bet - ter place, take a

look at your - self and then make the change. __ You got - ta get it right, __ while you got the time. __

close your heart __ then you close your mind! With that
You can't close your, your mind! That man, that

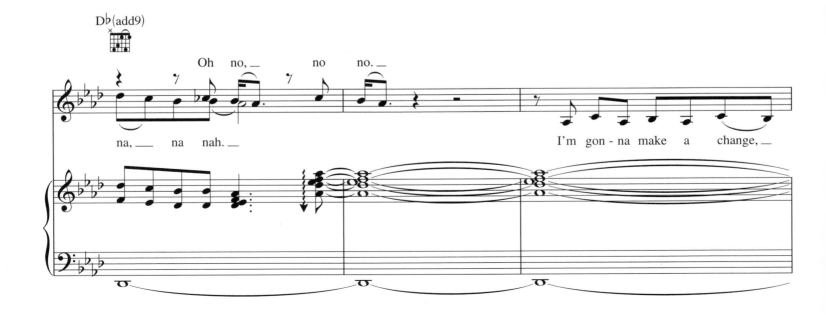

MANIC MONDAY

Words and Music by
PRINCE

NOTHING'S GONNA STOP US NOW

Words and Music by DIANE WARREN
and ALBERT HAMMOND

ROCK THE CASBAH

Words and Music by JOE STRUMMER,
MICK JONES and TOPPER HEADON

OH SHERRIE

Words and Music by STEVE PERRY, RANDY GOODRUM,
BILL CUOMO and CRAIG KRAMPF

273

ON THE WINGS OF LOVE

Words and Music by JEFFREY OSBORNE
and PETER SCHLESS

and I'm yours ___ ex - clu - sive - ly.___ And right now ___ we live ___ and

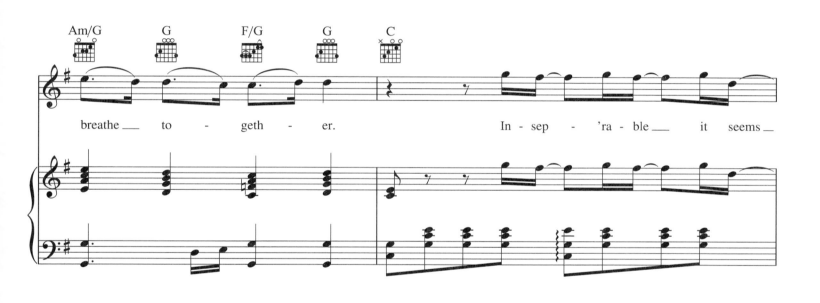

breathe ___ to - geth - er. In - sep - 'ra - ble ___ it seems ___

___ we're flow - ing like ___ a stream run - ning free trav - el - ing

RED, RED WINE

Words and Music by
NEIL DIAMOND

Slow Country beat

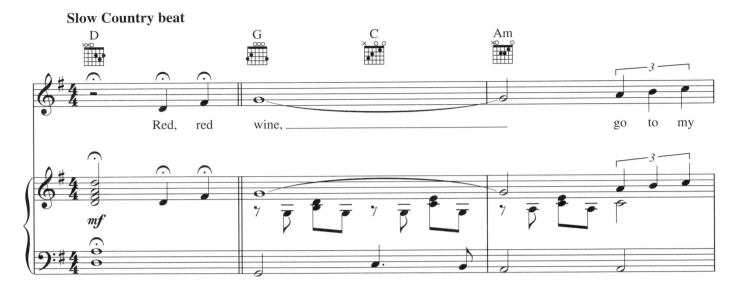

Red, red wine, _____ go to my

head, make me for - get that I

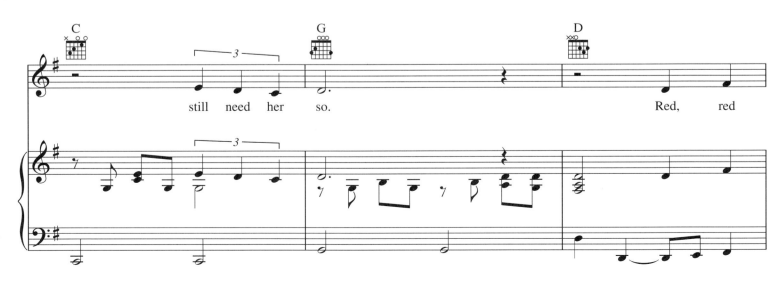

still need her so. Red, red

SAILING

Words and Music by
CHRISTOPHER CROSS

SISTER CHRISTIAN

Words and Music by
KELLY KEAGY

THE SEARCH IS OVER

Words and Music by JAMES M. PETERIK
and FRANK SULLIVAN

fi - n'lly struck _ like light - nin' from _ the blue; _____

ev- er- y high- way is lead- in' me back _ to you. _____

right be - fore _ my eyes.

SEVEN BRIDGES ROAD

Words and Music by
STEPHEN T. YOUNG

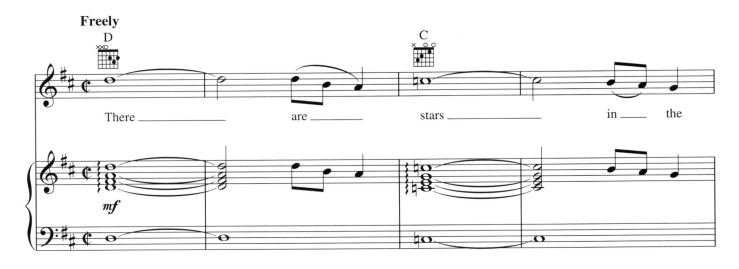

There _____ are _____ stars _____ in _____ the

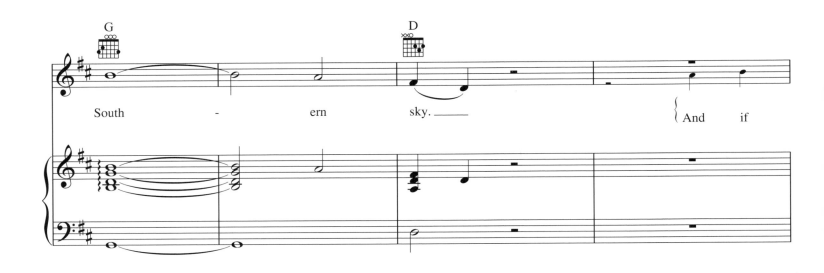

South - ern sky. _____ And if

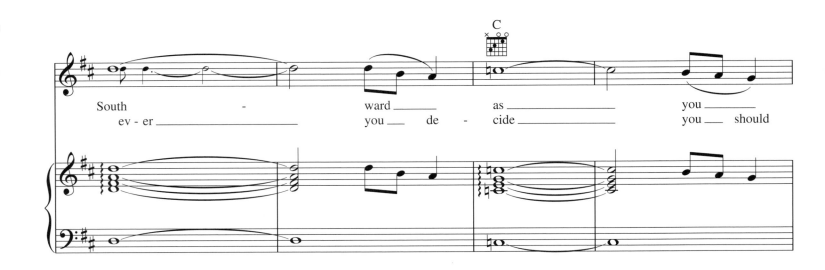

South - ward _____ as _____ you _____
ev - er _____ you de - cide _____ you _____ should

Bright Country

these _____ warm stars _____ down the

Sev - en _____ Bridg - es _____

Road. _____

D.C. al Coda

CODA

Road. _____

SHOULD I STAY OR SHOULD I GO

Words and Music by MICK JONES
and JOE STRUMMER

312

SMOOTH OPERATOR

Words and Music by HELEN ADU
and RAY ST. JOHN

SOMEWHERE OUT THERE

Words and Music by JAMES HORNER,
BARRY MANN and CYNTHIA WEIL

through, then we'll be to - geth - er some - where out there, out

where dreams come true. _____

323

STEPPIN' OUT

Words and Music by
JOE JACKSON

*Recorded a half step higher.

329

STRAY CAT STRUT

Words and Music by
BRIAN SETZER

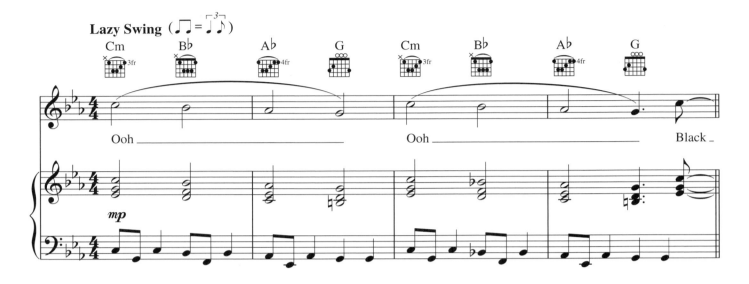

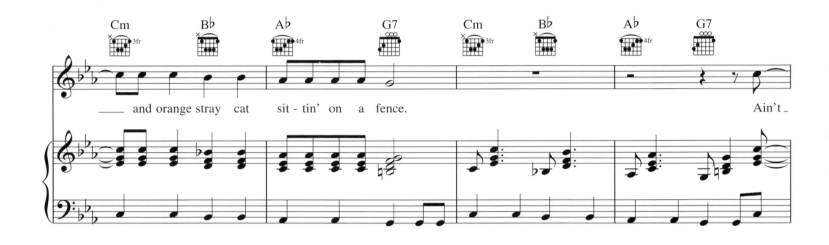

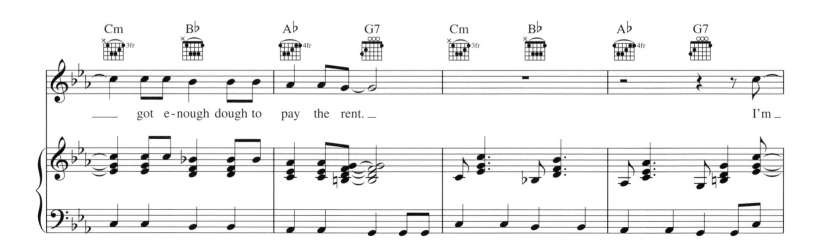

SWEET DREAMS
(Are Made Of This)

Words and Music by DAVID A. STEWART
and ANNIE LENNOX

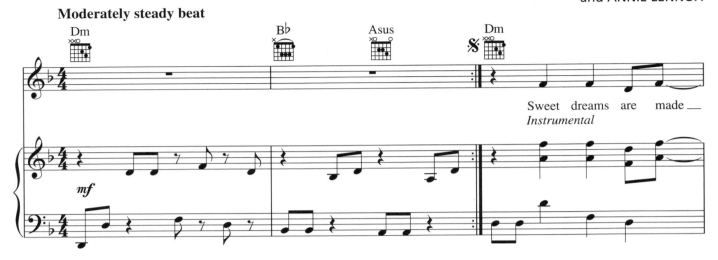

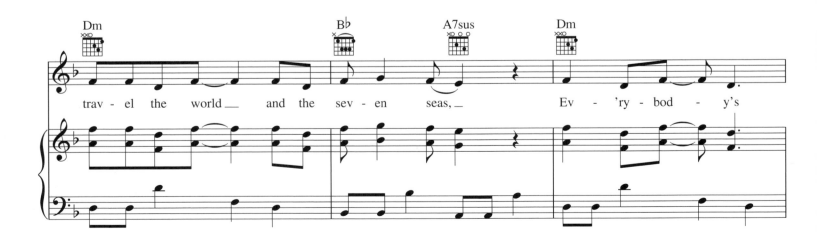

Hold your head up, mov - in' on. ___ Keep your head up, mov - in' on. ___

Hold your head up, mov - in' on. ___ Keep your head up, mov - in' on. ___

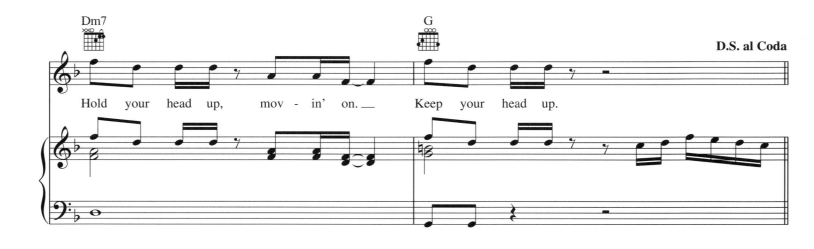

D.S. al Coda

Hold your head up, mov - in' on. ___ Keep your head up.

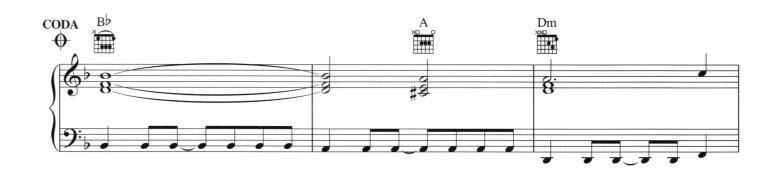

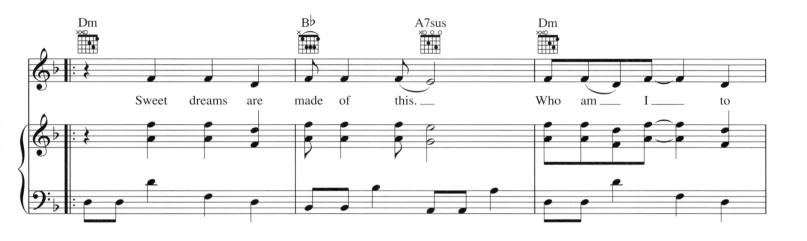

Sweet dreams are made of this. ___ Who am ___ I ___ to

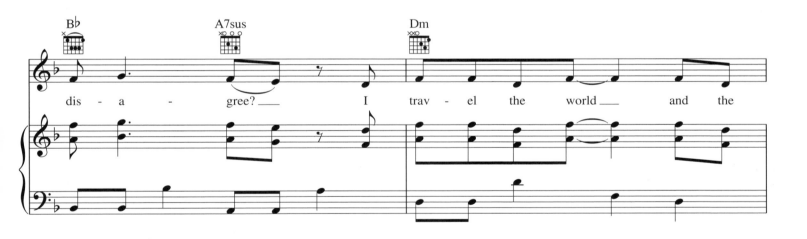

dis - a - gree? ___ I trav - el the world ___ and the

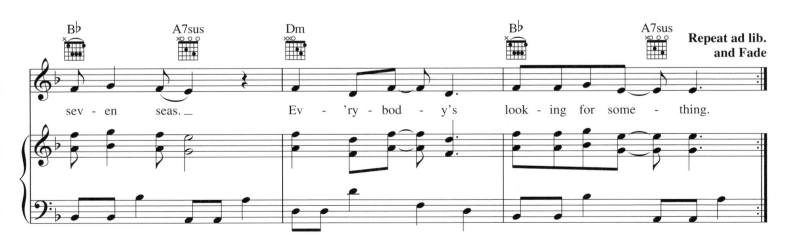

Repeat ad lib.
and Fade

sev - en seas. ___ Ev - 'ry - bod - y's look - ing for some - thing.

TAKE MY BREATH AWAY
from the Paramount Picture TOP GUN

Words and Music by GIORGIO MORODER
and TOM WHITLOCK

THRILLER

Words and Music by
ROD TEMPERTON

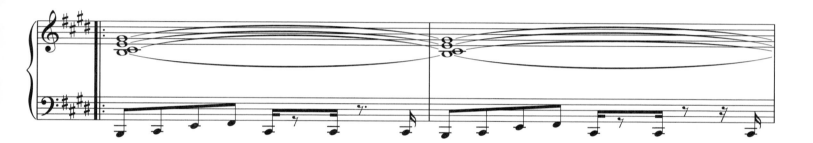

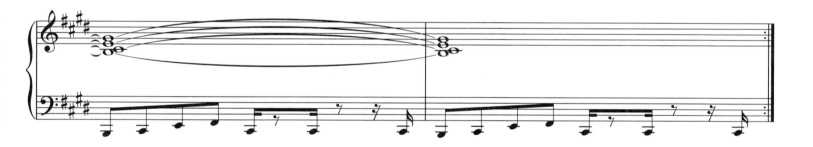

It's   close   to   mid   -   night,____   and
You   hear   the   door____   slam____   and
They're   out   to   get____   you.____   There's

some - thin' e - vil's lurk - in' in the dark. _____
re - al - ize there's no - where left to run. _____
de - mons clos - in' in on ev - 'ry side. _____

Un - der the moon - light _____ you
You feel the cold _____ hand, _____ and
They will pos - sess _____ you _____ un -

see a sight that al - most stops your heart. _____ You try to scream, _____
won - der if you'll ev - er see the sun. _____ You close your eyes, _____
less you change that num - ber on your dial. _____ Now is the time _____

but   ter - ror takes _ the sound _ be - fore _ you make _
and   hope that this _ is just _ i - mag - i - na -
for   you and I ___ to cud - dle close _ to - geth -

___ it. _____
- tion. _____
- er. _____

You   start to freeze _
But all   the while,
All through the night _

as   hor - ror looks _ you right _ be - tween _ the eyes. _
you   hear the crea - ture creep - in' up ___ be - hind. _
I'll   save you from _ the ter - ror on ___ the screen. _

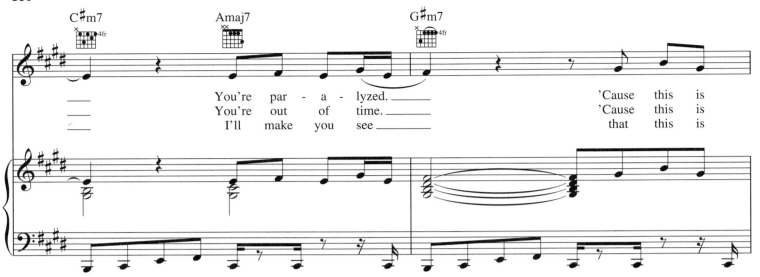

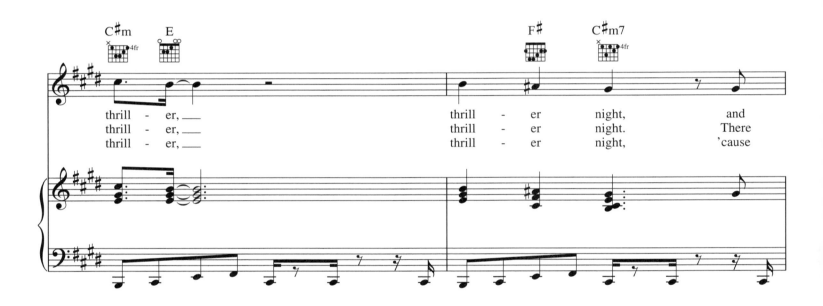

thrill - er, ___   thrill - er night.   You're
thrill - er, ___   thrill - er night.   You're
thrill - er, ___   thrill - er night,   so

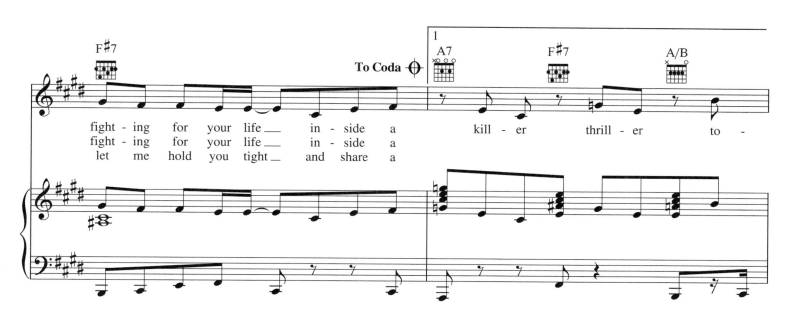

fight - ing for your life ___ in - side a   kill - er thrill - er to -
fight - ing for your life ___ in - side a   kill - er thrill - er to -
let me hold you tight ___ and share a

night. _____

Spoken Lyrics

1. Darkness falls across the land.
   The midnight hour is close at hand.
   Creatures crawl in search of blood
   To terrorize y'all's neighborhood.
   And whosoever shall be found
   Without the soul for getting down
   Must stand and face the hounds of hell
   And rot inside a corpse's shell.

2. The foulest stench is in the air,
   The funk of forty thousand years,
   And grizzly ghouls from every tomb
   Are closing in to seal your doom.
   And though you fight to stay alive,
   Your body starts to shiver,
   For no mere mortal can resist
   The evil of a thriller.

TIME AFTER TIME

Words and Music by CYNDI LAUPER
and ROB HYMAN

UP WHERE WE BELONG

from the Paramount Picture AN OFFICER AND A GENTLEMAN

Words by WILL JENNINGS
Music by BUFFY SAINTE-MARIE and JACK NITZSCHE

VIDEO KILLED THE RADIO STAR

Words and Music by BRUCE WOOLLEY,
TREVOR HORN and GEOFF DOWNES

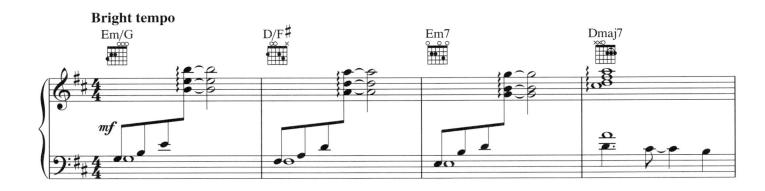

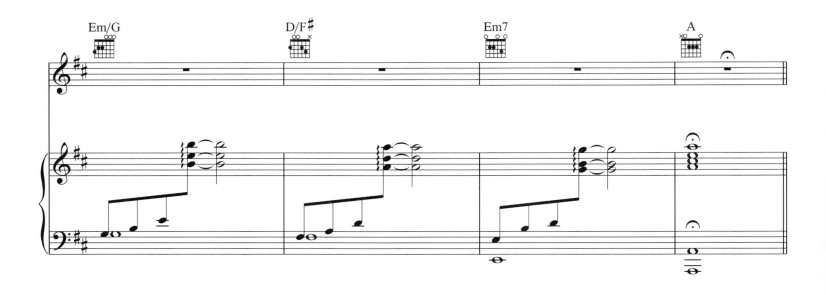

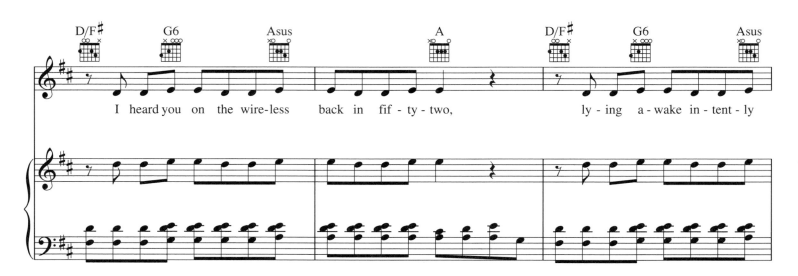

I heard you on the wire-less back in fif-ty-two, ly-ing a-wake in-tent-ly

Pic - tures came __ and broke __ your heart. __ Put the blame __ on

V. C. R. _____ You are _____

__ a ra - di - o star. _____ You

Vid - e - o killed the ra - di - o star.

Repeat and Fade

WALK LIKE AN EGYPTIAN

Words and Music by
LIAM STERNBERG

Guitar solo

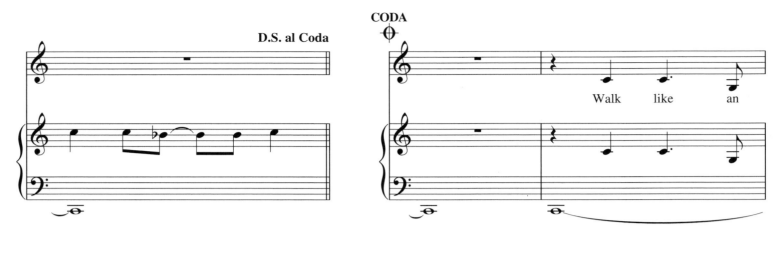

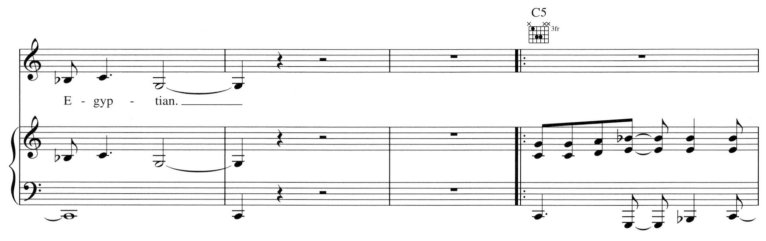

Additional Lyrics

3. The blond waitresses take their trays.
   They spin around and they cross the floor.
   They've got the moves, oh way oh.
   You drop your drink, then they bring you more.

4. All the schoolkids so sick of books,
   They like the punk and the metal band.
   Then the buzzer rings, oh way oh,
   They're walking like an Egyptian.

5. Slide your feet up the street, bend your back.
   Shift your arm, then you pull it back.
   Life's hard, you know, oh way oh,
   So strike a pose on a Cadillac.

6. If you want to find all the cops,
   They're hanging out in the donut shop.
   They sing and dance, oh way oh.
   They spin the club, cruise down the block.

7. All the Japanese with their yen,
   The party boys call the Kremlin.
   And the Chinese know, oh way oh,
   They walk the line like Egyptians.

WHAT'S LOVE GOT TO DO WITH IT

Words and Music by TERRY BRITTEN
and GRAHAM LYLE

Slow Rock

You must un - der - stand, though the touch of __ your hand __ makes my
may seem __ to you __ that I'm act - ing - con - fused __ when you're

pulse re - act, ___
close to __ me. __

that it's on - ly __ the thrill __ of
If I tend to __ look dazed, __ I

boy meet - ing girl, __ op - po - sites at - tract. __ It's
read it __ some - place, __ I got cause to __ be. __ There's a

WANTED DEAD OR ALIVE

Words and Music by JON BON JOVI
and RICHIE SAMBORA

It's

THE WARRIOR

Words and Music by NICK GILDER
and HOLLY KNIGHT

Chorus

Additional Lyrics

2. You talk, talk, you talk to me,
   Your eyes touch me physically.
   Stay with me, we'll take the night
   As passion takes another bite.
   Who's the hunter, who's the game?
   I feel the beat, call your name.
   I hold you close in victory.
   I don't wanna tame your animal style;
   You won't be caged in the call of the wild.
   Chorus

WE ARE THE WORLD

Words and Music by LIONEL RICHIE
and MICHAEL JACKSON

WHAT ABOUT LOVE

Words and Music by BRIAN ALLEN,
SHERON ALTON and JIM VALLANCE

402

What a-bout

share it with you.

Vocal ad lib: (What about love? *What about love?)*

WHITE WEDDING

Words and Music by
BILLY IDOL

Fast Rock

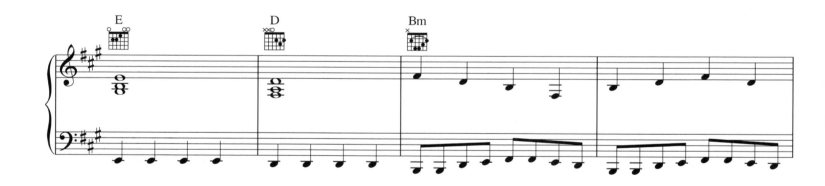

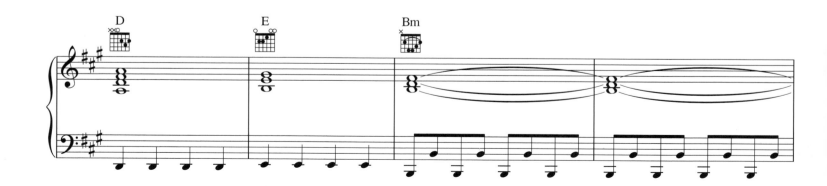

Hey lit - tle sis - ter, who's __ your su - per man?
Hey lit - tle sis - ter shot - gun oh __ yeah. __
I've been a - way for so ___ long so __ long. __

Hey lit - tle sis - ter, who's __ the one __ you want? Hey lit - tle sis - ter, shot -
Hey lit - tle sis - ter who's __ your su - per man? Hey lit - tle sis - ter shot -
I've been a - way for so ___ long so __ long. __ I let you go for so __

- gun!
- gun!
__ long.   It's a nice day to start __ a - gain. __

WHERE DO BROKEN HEARTS GO

Words and Music by CHUCK JACKSON
and FRANK WILDHORN

415